C000066077

The Box Hill and Mole Valley Book
of
Geology

Richard Selley

The Friends of Box Hill
2006

The author is Emeritus Professor of Geology and a Senior Research Fellow at Imperial College. He has lived in the Mole Valley for most of his life, apart from expeditions to the ends of the Earth exploring for petroleum, coal, gold, and water. In his retirement he researches the control of geology and climate change on viticulture.

ACKNOWLEDGEMENTS
I am grateful to Cliff Bayliss, Dr Jenny Huggett, Sandra Wedgwood and Lord Oxburgh for critical reviewing an early draft of this work, and to Lord Oxburgh for writing the foreword. Thanks are due to Sue Tatham for the skilful editing and design of this book, to Ben Tatham for taking the photographs and to Andrew Tatham for drawing the diagrams.

COVER PHOTOGRAPHS
Front cover: Box Hill viewed from Denbies vineyard
Inside front cover: The sandpit at Buckland
Back cover: A knapped flint wall

Copyright © 2006   Text: Richard C Selley
                     Illustrations: the author's except where otherwise stated.
                     Photographs: Ben Tatham (except Figures 1, 17 a) and b) ii, 19 b) and 21.)
                     Diagrams: Andrew Tatham

Designed by Sue Tatham
Published by The Friends of Box Hill, Pixham Mill, Dorking, Surrey RH4 1PQ
ISBN 0-9534430-6-X / 978-0-9534430-6-2 Printed in Dorking, Surrey by Summit Print Ltd.

CONTENTS

FOREWORD

Box Hill and the Mole Valley form part of the Surrey Hills Area of Outstanding Natural Beauty, and for centuries have attracted people in general and naturalists, writers and artists in particular. This beautiful landscape results from the interplay of climate and geology. The geology of the area has been described in the works of the British Geological Survey, and in many papers in the learned journals. There has not, until now however, been a book written to explain this landscape to the general reader. 'The Box Hill and Mole Valley Book of Geology' will fill this niche. It explains how the rocks were first deposited grain by grain and layer upon layer on deltas and sea floors. It shows how the strata were uplifted and eroded by running water and shaped during the Ice Age to produce the beautiful landscape of today. It describes how the rocks have provided a rich suite of industrial minerals, and a diversity of fauna and flora. The book also speculates on the near future as the Earth continues to warm, and on the distant future as erosion and subsidence return Box Hill and the Mole Valley to the sea from which they rose so many million years ago.

16 October 2006

One of my many character weaknesses is a devotion to the sport of orienteering and it so happens that Box Hill is a favourite area for planning orienteering courses. I therefore have a little personal familiarity with the area that is described. I say 'a little' because close interpretation of the landscape is not one's first preoccupation when finding a way as fast as possible (or not) through some of the intricacies of the topography. I was therefore doubly delighted to be invited to write the foreword to Professor Selley's account of the geology of the area. It will certainly stimulate me to return and to take a more leisurely and relaxed look at the rocks and the topography they support.

Richard Selley is a professional geologist of distinction. He has lived within sight of Box Hill for most of his life, apart from lengthy travels to the ends of the Earth. He has made his own mark upon the landscape of the Mole Valley. He is thus eminently well qualified to write this book, which I am delighted to commend.

Ron Oxburgh

Lord Oxburgh of Liverpool, KBE, FRS
Chairman, House of Lords Science & Technology Committee

PREFACE

'The Box Hill and Mole Valley Book of Geology' originated in the keynote lecture for the Heritage Weekend in September 2005. The theme of the weekend was 'Sticks and Stones'. The title of the lecture was 'Mole Valley Rocks: key to landscape, environment and resources'. The venue was Denbies Winery, naturally. Over 150 people applied for tickets. Sadly only 100 could be accommodated. Subsequently the lecture has been repeated many times in Dorking and the surrounding villages. The Friends of Box Hill have kindly asked for the lecture to be turned into a book. 'The Box Hill and Mole Valley Book of Geology' thus joins their excellent series of publications that describe every –ology of Box Hill. This book is written for the general reader who is interested in understanding how this very special landscape has formed, not only richly blessed with beautiful scenery, but also with a cornucopia of natural resources. Professional geologists may also find this work of interest, but will note that I have glossed over some of the more complex and contentious aspects of the local geology, partly on purpose, partly through ignorance.

It has been remarked that mankind inhabits this planet by courtesy of its geology. There is a geological reason for every hill and valley on Earth. The Mole Valley is no exception. The North Downs, the Holmesdale and the Surrey Hills, through which the Mole flows, reflect the differential erosion of chalk, clay and sandstone. Each rock type generates its own scenery, soil type, wildlife, vegetation – and hence agriculture. Geology explains why there are grass snakes on the North Downs and adders in the Surrey Hills, why the North Downs are dissected by extensive river valleys that lack rivers, why Dorking has been famous for poultry, why there is a bat colony in the Westhumble caves, why the River Mole vanishes through its bed in dry summers, why there is a vineyard at Denbies, why there is a gas field at Albury, and why there are caves in Dorking, but not Leatherhead.

Mole Valley and its hinterland are rich in natural resources provided by its diverse geology. Over its history this area has produced bricks, glass, building sand, fuller's earth, lime, firestone, hearthstone, iron, water, natural gas, oil, phosphates and witch repellent.

Casual readers are often nervous of '–ologies' in general, and of 'geology' in particular. It may therefore be helpful to calm down such persons by pointing out that most people are already incipient geologists. Anyone who lives in or around the Mole Valley knows that Box Hill is made of chalk, and that in dry summers the water of the River Mole seeps into fissures in its bed around Burford Bridge. Anyone who lives in or around the Mole Valley knows that Leith Hill, the Nower and Deepdene are made of sandstone. Everyone knows something about volcanoes, earthquakes, tsunamis, ice ages and climate change, about dinosaurs, and their postulated extinction due to a comet. Most people can tell a trilobite from an ammonite, and granite from slate. Well all of that is geology. Everyone knows something about geology, even journalists who love to talk about 'seismic shifts' of policy and 'tectonic plates' of public opinion without having a clue what they are. So do not panic. Relax and read on. At the end of the book is a glossary and a section of FAQs (Frequently Asked Questions) to answer just those.

Richard Selley
August 2006

INTRODUCTION: WHAT IS IN A NAME?

The etymology of place names is full of intellectual elephant traps. The name Box Hill, however, is as simple as it suggests. Box is an Old English word for the Box tree, *Buxus sempervirens*. The box is a native of the Mediterranean and the Far East, and is a popular garden shrub in England. It grows wild in southern England, however, especially on well-drained south-facing sunny limestone slopes, such as Box Hill.

The name of the River Mole, however, is an etymological elephant trap. The simple explanation is that the name refers to the Mole's habit of vanishing underground, especially in times of drought (something to be described later in this book). This explanation can be traced back at least a far as the mid-eighteenth century, where a fulsome article on the Mole Valley in the 'Gentleman's Magazine' provides this explanation. Sadly it is wrong. There are two quite different and much older explanations. The first is that the name has migrated upriver from Molesey, where the River Mole flows into the Thames. Recorded as *Muleseg* in 672-4, translating as 'Island or dry ground in Marsh, or of a man called '*Mul*'' (Mills, 2003). An alternative suggestion is that the name derives from the Old English '*Melyn*' meaning 'mill' (Latin *Mola*). Perhaps originally *Y Melyn* – River of Mills. There were 20 mills recorded on the River Mole in the Domesday Book (Brayley, 1850).

Having pointed out the popular misconception for the etymology of the River Mole it is irresistible to suggest an origin for Ranmore Common, Box Hill's counterpart on the opposite side of the Mole Valley. Speakers of Gaelic or Erse, the old pre-Roman Celtic tongue of the British Isles, will note that it sounds like '*Roinn mhor*', which translates as 'big ridge'. A more apposite name for Ranmore would be hard to find.

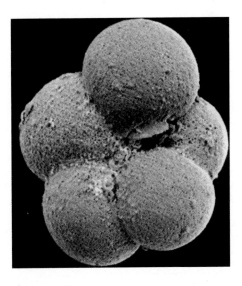

Figure 1 *Tennuitellinata selleyi* (magnified x 100). Some 10 million years ago, while the chalk of the Weald was being uplifted and the landscape of Box Hill and the Mole Valley dissected, the microscopic foraminifer *T. selleyi* drifted around in the sea alternating idylls of idleness with moments of frenzied procreation.

THE DEPOSITION OF THE SEDIMENTARY STRATA OF THE MOLE VALLEY

The River Mole rises in the Weald and drains into the River Thames at Molesey. On its way it cuts through the big ridge of the North Downs separating Box Hill to the east from Ranmore Common to the west. The North Downs defines the northern flank of the up-fold (anticline) of sedimentary strata of the Weald, and the southern limb of the large down-fold (syncline) of the London Basin. The strata involved in these folds are all of Cretaceous age (deposited broadly between 140 and 70 million years ago). The North Downs are composed of a resistant ridge of Chalk, a variety of limestone. The Chalk overlies the thin Upper Greensand, which has little effect on landscape. At the foot of the North Downs an east-west aligned valley, termed the Holmesdale, was eroded in the soft impermeable Gault Clay, across which the River

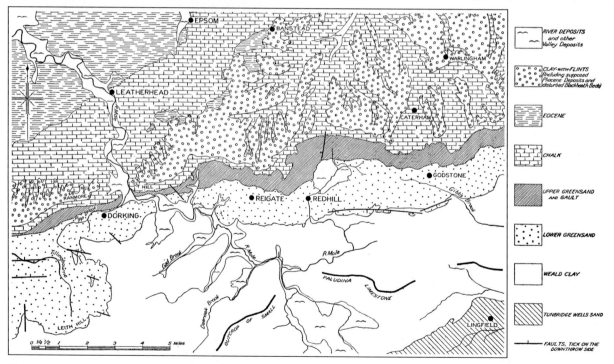

Figure 2 Geological map of Box Hill, the Mole Valley and its hinterland. From Dines & Edmunds (1933). Courtesy of the British Geological Survey.

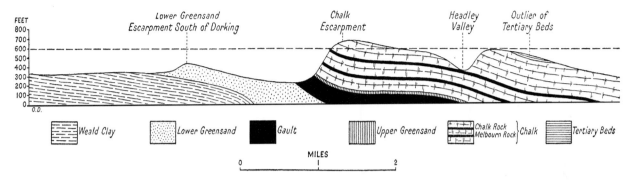

Figure 3 South to North geological cross-section through Box Hill to show how the alternating hard and soft strata have been preserved and eroded respectively to form a series of south-facing escarpments and intervening dip slopes and valleys. From Dines & Edmunds (1933). Courtesy of the British Geological Survey.

Mole flows towards Dorking from the east, and the Pipp Brook from the west. Beneath the Gault Clay is the Lower Greensand. This forms the line of the Surrey Hills, reaching their zenith at Leith Hill, and separates the Holmesdale from the Weald Clay of the Weald.

To understand the formation of the Mole Valley and Box Hill it is essential to describe the rocks that determine the landscape and its resources. The oldest rocks that crop out at the surface of the Mole Valley are the Early Cretaceous Wealden sediments. The youngest rocks that the Mole flows across after leaving the North Downs are the London Clay and Bagshot Sands of Eocene age. This sequence of rocks is illustrated in Figure 4 on the next page.

The River Mole rises close to Gatwick Airport and flows north and west across the Wealden sediments. These are heavy grey clays, about 300 metres thick, with thin inter-beds of sandstone and limestone of Early Cretaceous age (some 120-130 million years old). The clays contain a diverse range of fossils, including plants such as *Equisetites*, a relative of the modern Horsetail fern. This sometimes occurs above fossil soil horizons and associated with strata showing shrinkage cracks due to exposure to sunlight. The fossils include a range of freshwater bivalves, such as *Unio*, gastropods, such as the freshwater snail *Viviparus* (Syn. *Paludina*), insects, and some spectacularly horrible dinosaurs, such as *Iguanodon* and *Baryonyx*. *Iguanodon* was first found and described in Sussex, and was the first giant reptile to be called a dinosaur in 1841. *Baryonyx* was discovered in 1983 at Smokejacks Brickworks near Ockley. With its long talons it is colloquially called 'Jaws'. *Baryonyx* is believed to have sat in the bog using its long claws to scoop up fish from streams; the dinosaur precursor of Gollum.

Within the Weald clays there are thin beds of limestone packed full of the freshwater snail *Viviparus* (Syn. *Paludina*). Within the Weald Clay

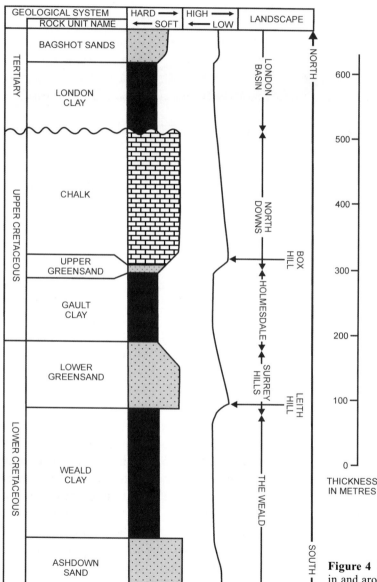

GEOLOGICAL SYSTEM	ROCK UNIT NAME	HARD → ← SOFT	HIGH → ← LOW	LANDSCAPE

there are also thin layers of siderite nodules, iron carbonate ($FeCO_3$). This is commonly found in shallow brackish environments.

The Wealden fauna and flora, together with sun cracks and fossilised soils, indicate deposition in a shallow lake, with marginal marshes and sand flats. Boreholes in northern Surrey and the Thames Valley show that the Wealden, and later, Cretaceous sediments thin out and terminate. Traced south across the English Channel into France, they thicken and become more marine. These changes indicate at this time an east-west trending shoreline extended through what was to become the Mole Valley. The Wealden sediments are arranged in upward coarsening sequences of clay, silt and sand. Each sequence is capped by a horizon with desiccation cracks and the rhizomes of *Equisetites*. These sequences indicate repeated shallowing of the lake as shoreline sands, with emergent swamps, prograded out across quieter deeper water muds. At its top the Wealden deposits contain ammonites, indicative of marine conditions. This topmost unit, the Atherfield Clay, heralds the change from the fresh water conditions of the Wealden sediments to the marine environment of the succeeding Lower Greensand.

Figure 4 Diagram of the sequence of rocks that crop out in and around the Mole Valley, youngest at the top, oldest at the bottom.

6

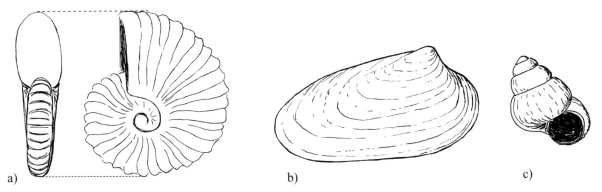

Figure 5 Fossils from the Wealden Series: a) the ammonite *Deshayites deshahi* from the marine Atherfield clay at the top of the Wealden sequence x 0.75, b) the freshwater bivalve *Unio* x 0.75, c) the freshwater gastropod *Viviparus (Paludina)*, which occurs abundantly in thin beds of limestone, the so-called Purbeck Marble x 1.25.

The Lower Greensand

Towards the top the Wealden Series shows increasing evidence of deposition in a marine environment, passing up into the wholly marine Atherfield Clay, which is, confusingly, taken as the lowest unit of the Lower Greensand Group. At the boundary between the impermeable Atherfield Clay and the porous, permeable Lower Greensand proper, there is a line of springs, and associated landslips, along the Leith Hill escarpment. The Lower Greensand is about 100 metres thick, of Early Cretaceous age, and was deposited between 110 and 120 million years ago. The Lower Greensand gets its name because it contains many rounded green grains of the mineral glauconite. This is composed of iron, magnesium and other elements. Glauconite is important because it only forms in shallow seas, and is, therefore, an important environmental indicator. Most of the Lower Greensand is well cemented with lime ($CaCO_3$) and chert (silica, SiO_2), thus giving rise to

the Surrey Hills that stretch eastwards from Farnham. Locally they form Leith Hill, the Nower and the Deepdene. Most of the Lower Greensand consists of alternating hard cemented and soft un-cemented strata, termed 'rag' and 'hassock' respectively. 'Rag', or 'ragstone' is an important local building stone. The Lower Greensand also contains horizons of degraded volcanic ash, termed 'fuller's earth'.

The uppermost unit of the Lower Greensand is composed of the soft rusty yellow sands of the Folkestone Beds, so names because the type locality at which they crop out is Folkestone, within which glauconite is largely absent. These beds crop out in a series of quarries through Dorking. Gluconite is absent because it is unstable in the presence of rainwater. This dissolves the mineral grains carrying its components off in solution. The iron often re-precipitates as rusty iron oxide (limonite) cement between the quartz (silica, SiO_2) sand grains. The

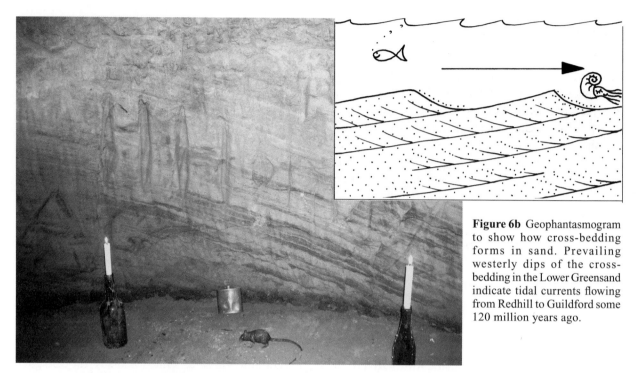

Figure 6b Geophantasmogram to show how cross-bedding forms in sand. Prevailing westerly dips of the cross-bedding in the Lower Greensand indicate tidal currents flowing from Redhill to Guildford some 120 million years ago.

Figure 6a Photograph of cross-bedded sandstone exposed in the wall of the 'Mystery chamber' in Dorking's famous South Street caves.

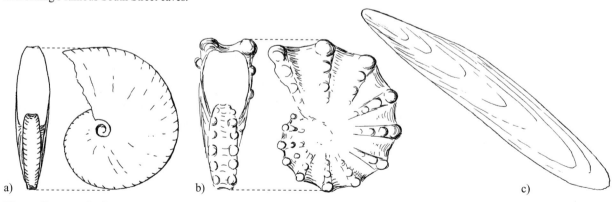

Figure 7 Fossils from the Lower Greensand. a) the ammonite *Anahoplites planus* x 0.75, *b)* the ammonite *Douvilleiceras unaequinoides* x 0.75, *c)* the bivalve *Gervillia* x 1.0.

The Gault Clay

The Lower Greensand is overlain by the Gault Clay. This unit is about 100 metres thick in the Mole Valley area, and was deposited some 110-100 million years ago. As noted above, the dissolution of glauconite at the top of the Lower Greensand indicates uplift and flushing by rainwater. This evidence of a break in deposition is confirmed by the fact that the boundary between the two units is sharp, and often marked by a horizon of gravel.

The Gault Clay is sticky, heavy blue-grey clay with an interesting and abundant fauna that includes bivalves and ammonites. The ammonites indicate a marine environment, and the fine grain size suggests deposition in relatively deep and quiet conditions. The fossils are often replaced by phosphate. Phosphatised fossils and nodules occur both disseminated throughout the Gault Clay, and also concentrated in horizons.

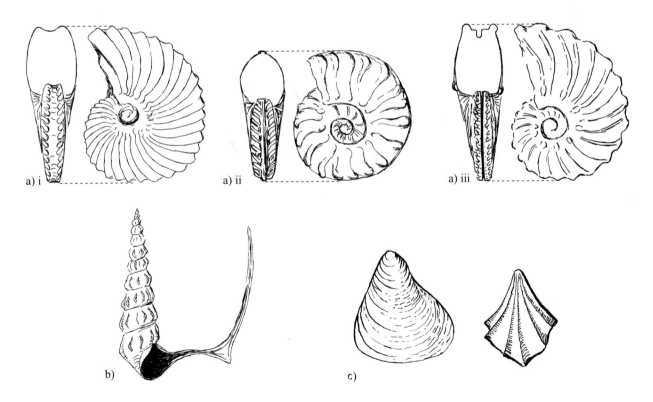

Figure 8 Fossils from the Gault Clay. a) Ammonites: i *Hoplites interruptus* x 0.75, ii *Hysteroceras variacasus* x 4.0, iii *Euhoplites lautus* x 1. b) The gastropod *Rostellaria (Tibia) carinata* x 0.75, c) Two *Inoceramid* bivalves, both x 1.0.

The Upper Greensand

The Gault Clay passes gradationally up into the Upper Greensand. This is about only a few metres thick in the Mole Valley area and has a negligible topographic expression, occurring at the foot of the North Downs. Its location is marked by a spring line, the so-called 'winterbournes'. This is where the permeable Chalk and Upper Greensand overlie the impermeable Gault Clay. The spring that feeds the Silent Pool at Albury is one such example. As its name suggests, the Upper Greensand contains grains of glauconite like the Lower Greensand. This fact, together with fossils such as ammonites, indicates that it was deposited beneath the sea. There are two important varieties of Upper Greensand. One is well-cemented white siliceous sand. This was quarried

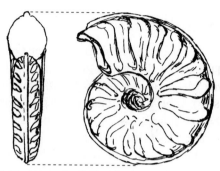

Figure 9 The ammonite *Schloenbachia rostrata* from the Upper Greensand x 1.25.

locally for 'Firestone', being suitable as a refractory brick that could withstand high temperatures. The second variety is soft pure white sand. This was quarried locally as 'Hearthstone', being used for whitening hearths and doorsteps (Sowan, 1975).

The Chalk

The Chalk of the North Downs will be familiar to all inhabitants of the Mole Valley and the wider world. It is a spectacular rock of almost global distribution, and, as in the Mole Valley, commonly passes down via glauconitic sandstones to a major depositional break. The Chalk is of Late Cretaceous age, and was deposited between about 100 and 60 million years ago. It originally extended from Ireland and northwest Scotland across most of northern Europe and beyond. Subsequent erosion has removed the Chalk from many areas, as in the Weald. Elsewhere it has been preserved by burial beneath younger sediments, as in the London, Hampshire and Paris basins.

The Chalk is a friable pure white fine-grained limestone. It is very light and 'chalky' compared with other limestones. This is because it is highly porous, with porosities of up to 40%. Because of the small size of the pores chalk is naturally impermeable. Where the Chalk is fractured, however, it is highly permeable. This is why it is such an important aquifer in southern England and elsewhere. Chalk is composed of the skeletal remains of calcareous marine algae termed coccolithophorids. Individual fossils are termed coccospheres. They are composed of individual plates termed coccoliths, each one a single crystal of calcite ($CaCO_3$).

The chalk also contains a wide range of larger fossils, including fish, ammonites, sponges, sea urchins, marine snails and bivalves. A particular feature of the chalk is the occurrence of nodular layers

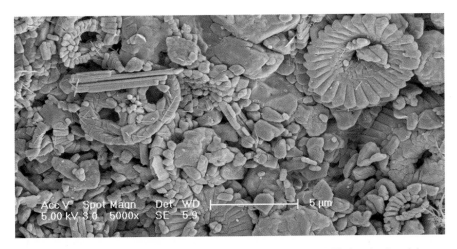

Figure 10 Scanning electron microscope photograph of chalk from Box Hill, showing how it is composed of the calcareous skeletal plates of coccolithophorid algae. Most are disaggregated; some are still articulated coccospheres. (One micron is one millionth of a metre.) Courtesy of J Huggett. Petroclays.

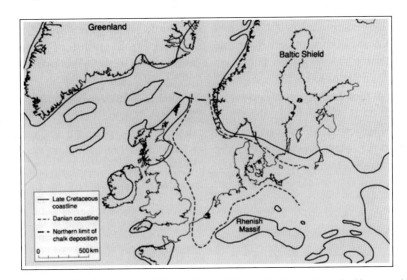

Figure 11 Map to show the distribution of the sea from which the Chalk was deposited between 100 and 60 million years ago. The Danian coastline was the youngest extent of Chalk deposition in the post-Cretaceous Palaeocene period. Reprinted from Encyclopedia of Geology. Ed. by Selley RC, Cocks, LRM & Plimer, IR. Vol. 5. Chalk. By Ineson, JR, Stemmerik, Surlyk, L & F. 42-50. © Elsevier 2005.

of chert, known locally as flint. Chert is a variety of silica (SiO_2) that clearly formed within chalk after it had been deposited. It is generally accepted that chert forms from the dissolution of siliceous sponges, followed by replacement of Chalk by flint. This sometimes occurs replacing fossil shells, and sometimes infilling the space within fossil shells, such as sea urchins, or infilling animal burrows on the seabed. It is the last of these that form the layers of tabular flints seen in some cliffs and quarries.

Occasionally rusty metallic spheres, several centimetres in diameter, are found in the Chalk. When smitten open they show a metallic radiating pattern.

Simple country folk often believe that these are meteorites fallen from the heavens, that splashed and sank into the Chalk sea. They formed in fact like flints, as concretions that grew within the Chalk mud subsequent to deposition. The metallic mineral is pyrites (FeS_2), often referred to as 'fool's gold'. Examination with a magnifying glass reveals that the crystals radiate from a fossil fragment or some such nucleus.

The Chalk also contains purple kidney-shaped lumps, colloquially termed 'kidney stone'. This is the iron oxide haematite (Fe_2O_3). It does not occur in sufficient abundance to be a commercial ore.

The Tertiary sediments

On reaching Leatherhead the flood plain of the River Mole widens as it is no longer restricted by the resistant Chalk of the North Downs. Here it passes from the Cretaceous Chalk onto soft clays and sands of Tertiary age. Geologically there is a major break in deposition. Much of the upper part of the Chalk that was deposited and preserved in other parts of Europe is absent in southeast England. Similarly strata of the earliest and oldest Tertiary sediments are absent. The youngest chalk is some 75 million years old, and the oldest Tertiary sediments are some 60 million years old, a gap of some 15 million years. This is unfortunate since within this gap lies the famous KT (Cretaceous:Tertiary) boundary. This was the time when the dinosaurs, which were already in decline, were finally extinguished, possibly assisted by a meteorite that landed at Chicxulub, Mexico, some 65 million years ago.

The Cretaceous:Tertiary unconformity, as such a break in deposition is termed, has had a major controlling effect on the development of Surrey in general, and the Mole Valley in particular. The unconformity can be traced from Guildford via Leatherhead to Epsom and Sutton. It is marked by a line of parish churches, villages and an old road, now the A246 and part of the A24. The aboriginal settlers of Surrey could not spell geology, but they clearly identified and delineated the boundary between the well-drained limey soil of the Cretaceous Chalk of the North Downs and the heavy soils of the London Clay. Originally there was a spring line at the unconformity, now gone as the water table of the London basin has sunk. A further attraction of the KT boundary for settlement by the aboriginal Surrey folk is some 20 metres of sand that separates the Chalk from the London Clay. This crops out in a strip about half a mile wide to provide light relatively easily cultivatable soil.

The Cretaceous:Tertiary unconformity was exposed in several Chalk quarries along the line of the modern A246. Most of these are now infilled. Below the unconformity the Chalk possesses many solution pipes, often infilled with glauconitic clay, now dissolved to rust. Good examples can be seen in the cutting beside the slip road where the A217 enters the eastbound M25 at Junction 8. (Health & Safety warning: Do not stop, and do not look for these if you are driving.) Above the unconformity is a bed of glauconite-encrusted flints. This is overlain by some 20 metres of sands of the Thanet and Reading Beds. These are soft sands with traces of glauconite and a diverse suite of fossils indicating deposition in a shallow sea. The Reading beds are overlain by about 100 metres of the London Clay.

This contains a rare but diverse fossil assemblage, including marine bivalves, together with fossilised turtles, crocodiles and terrestrial plants such as mangroves and vines. At Cobham the River Mole flows through an escarpment of Bagshot Sands in Painshill Park.

The Bagshot Sands are some 30 metres thick and generate a south-facing escarpment rising north to the Woking Wolds and the Heights of Hersham. The Mole meanders its way through the Bagshot Sands to enter the River Thames at Molesey. The Bagshot Sands contain a sparse marine fauna and were deposited some 45-50 million years ago.

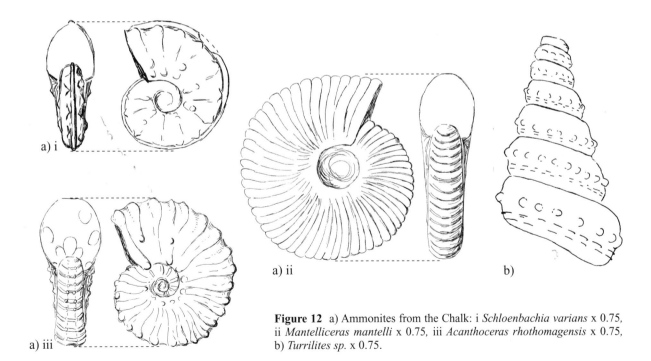

Figure 12 a) Ammonites from the Chalk: i *Schloenbachia varians* x 0.75, ii *Mantelliceras mantelli* x 0.75, iii *Acanthoceras rhothomagensis* x 0.75, b) *Turrilites sp.* x 0.75.

THE UPLIFT OF THE WEALD AND THE EROSION OF BOX HILL AND THE MOLE VALLEY

The Early Cretaceous sediments were deposited in a basin centred over what is now the Weald. They were largely derived from a landmass that lay to the north. Now it is a common feature of the Earth's crust that what goes down, must come up, facetiously referred to as 'yo-yo' tectonics, or more learnedly as 'an axis of inversion'. By the Late Cretaceous, some 65 million years ago, subsidence had largely ceased in the Wealden basin. The Chalk was deposited over northwest Euroland with a great uniformity of stratification. Individual beds only a few centimetres thick can be traced from the Chilterns to the south side of the Paris basin and beyond. At the end of the Cretaceous Period, however, the Earth's crust began to move. Inversion began. The ridge of land that had extended from Wales across to Belgium began to subside, and the Wealden basin began to dome upwards. As the core of the Wealden anticline (the name given to an up-fold of strata) was eroded the Chalk was stripped off to expose deeper sand and clay strata which were eroded in turn. Rivers carried the resultant detritus draining off the flanks of the Weald. Some rivers drained south into what was to become the English Channel, others north into the newly subsiding Thames basin.

The sequence of illustrations on the following pages shows how the core of the Wealden anticline was initially breached with a canoe-shaped valley. Over millions of years the Chalk escarpments of the North and South Downs migrated north and south respectively. It is tempting to think that their present position is a snapshot of a continuous if slowly moving process. The truth is rather more complex. The Wealden basin formed by the intermittent movement of a number of east-to-west aligned faults in the Earth's crust parallel to the basin margin. As the basin became inverted the faults began to move in the opposite direction. One such fault system extends along the foot of the North Downs from the Hog's Back, via Ranmore Common and Box Hill eastwards. The recent (15th C) earthquake at Reigate demonstrates that this fault is still active.

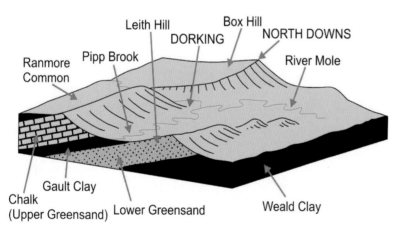

Figure 13 Geophantasmogram of Dorking and its surroundings showing the relationship between geology and scenery. Interbedded sedimentary strata of the Cretaceous Period dip north forming the northern limb of the Wealden anticline, the southern limb of the London basin. Well-cemented hard strata form hills, soft sediments form valleys.

Figure 14 View from White Down showing Dorking on the right and (from left) Ranmore, Box Hill, and Colley Hill with Reigate Hill in the far distance.

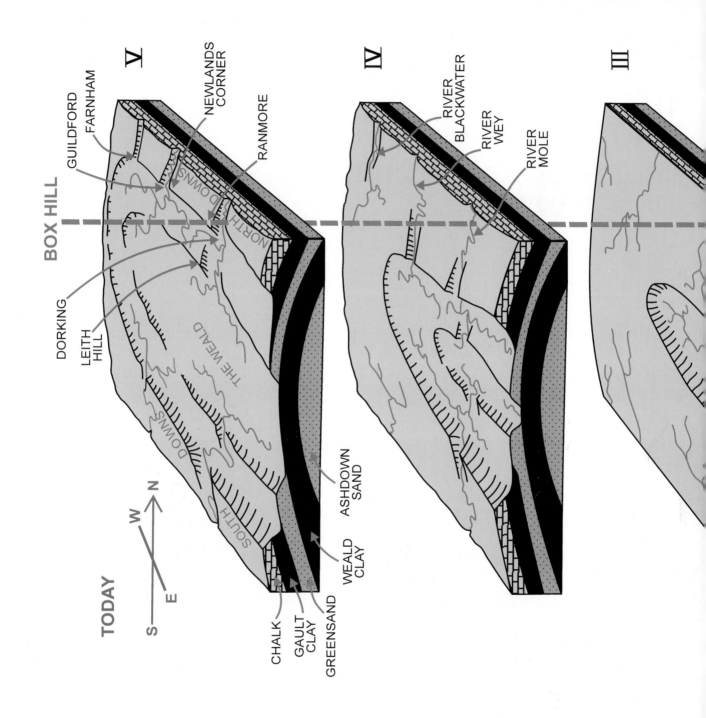

TODAY

V

BOX HILL

GUILDFORD
FARNHAM
NEWLANDS CORNER
RANMORE
DORKING
LEITH HILL
NORTH DOWNS
THE WEALD
SOUTH DOWNS

CHALK
GAULT CLAY
GREENSAND
WEALD CLAY
ASHDOWN SAND

N
W — E
S

IV

RIVER BLACKWATER
RIVER WEY
RIVER MOLE

III

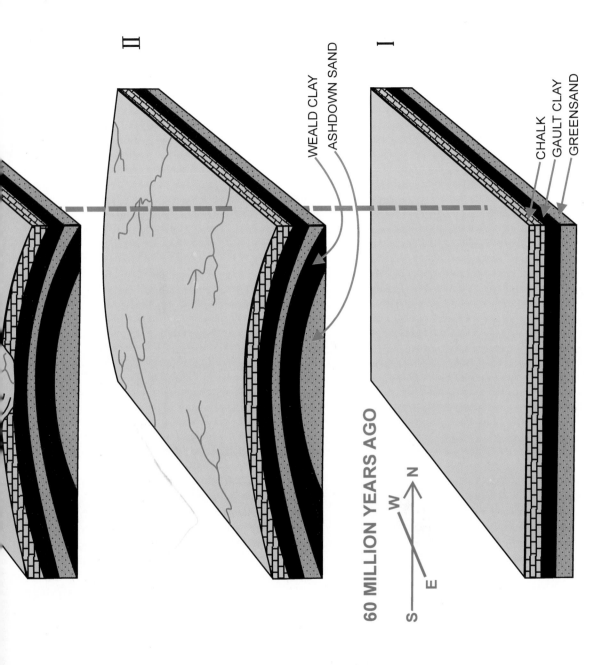

II

I

WEALD CLAY
ASHDOWN SAND

CHALK
GAULT CLAY
GREENSAND

60 MILLION YEARS AGO

N
W
S
E

Figure 15 Geophantasmograms to show the uplift and erosion of the Wealden anticline. Note the River Mole draining out between Box Hill and Ranmore Common. The River Wey, to the west of the Mole, eroded westwards along the Holmesdale to capture the headwaters of the Blackwater. This is why Farnham, though a 'gap' town like Guildford and Dorking, lacks its own river. The truncated Blackwater is an insignificant stream rising north of the North Downs.

THE MOLE VALLEY IN THE ICE AGE

Concomitant with the rise of the Wealden anticline throughout the last 60 million years there has been a gradual if erratic drop in temperature. For the last 2 million years the Earth has entered an Ice Age. Several such episodes of low temperature have been identified in the Earth's history. During the present Ice Age there have been numerous fluctuations in temperature, with the British Isles alternately enjoying temperatures sometimes warmer, sometimes much colder than obtain today. During the glacial maxima the British Isles have been covered by an ice sheet up to 2,000 metres thick in Scotland and 1,000 metres thick in Wales. The glaciers never advanced south of the Thames Valley and into the Home Counties. During these glacial episodes however, southern England was largely tundra, its ground frozen. The inhabitants included woolly mammoths, rhinoceroses, bears, wolves, deer and hungry itinerant hairy hominids.

The Ice Age left its imprint on the Mole Valley with both erosive and depositional features. The distinctive mammilated landscape of the Chalk has been remarked upon by many natural scientists. The Reverend Gilbert White, author of 'The Natural History and Antiquities of Selborne' (1789), commented:

'I think that there is somewhat peculiarly sweet and amusing in the shapely figured aspect of the chalk hills... I never contemplate these mountains without thinking I perceive somewhat analogous to growth in their gentle swellings and smooth fungus-like protuberances, their fluted sides, and regular hollows and slopes, that carry at once the air of vegetative dilation and expansion. Or was there ever time when these immense masses of calcareous matter were thrown into fermentation by some adventitious moisture...'

Rev G White, letter to the Hon. Daines Barrington
9 December 1773

Though one of the greatest naturalists of his day, Gilbert White's account displays greater powers of observation and expression than of deduction.

One of the most distinctive features of the Chalk downs are their dry valleys; valleys that as their name implies, curiously lack rivers. This poses the question of how can a valley be eroded in the absence of running water? The answer lies in the past climate. During the glacial maxima, when glaciers advanced to the Thames Valley, the tundra of southern England was frozen to a depth of several metres. In summer, however, the surface of the chalk would warm sufficiently for the surface snow to melt, and for the melt water to flow down hill carving river valleys on its way to the sea. During the warm interglacial periods, such as the one we presently enjoy, the permafrost has melted. Surface water is now free to sink down through the fractured chalk leaving the valleys dry and their further erosion limited.

Evidence of periglacial climate is not only to be found in the erosive features of the landscape, but also in sediments. On the top of the North Downs the Chalk is locally veneered by a thin layer of sediment termed 'Clay-with-flints'. It is just that, though it contains some sand, occasional Tertiary fossils and sandstone fragments. The origin of Clay-with-flints is curious. Obviously the flints are derived from the Chalk, but it is hard to understand a depositional process that allows the transport and deposition of flint cobbles and clay, with relatively little sand. It is now accepted that Clay-with-flints resulted from several different processes. It overlies the Chalk with an irregular surface pock-marked by solution swallow-holes. This suggests that it is, in part, an insoluble residue of the Chalk itself. There is more to it than this, however,

Figure 16 The Zig Zag Road in the early morning. For centuries travellers have used this route through a dry valley to reach the top of Box Hill.

Bones from the Pleistocene River Terrace gravels of the River Mole

Figure 17 a) Femurs of a mammoth (top right)
and a woolly rhinoceros (bottom left).

b) i Mammoth tooth showing grinding surface uppermost (left) and ii bisected segments (right).

From the Lord Ashcombe Collection, courtesy of the Dorking Museum.

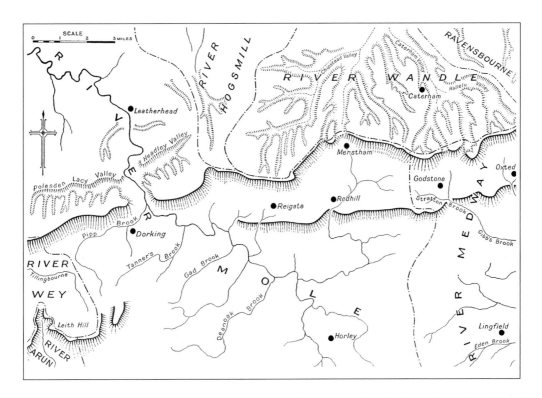

Figure 18 Map of the Mole Valley and its hinterland showing the dry valley systems of the Chalk downlands. From Dines & Edmunds (1933). Courtesy of the British Geological Survey. Note particularly the Polesden Lacey and Headley dry valleys that drained into the Mole Valley. These dry valleys were cut by seasonal rivers of melt water during glacial episodes of the present Ice Age.

as it is also necessary to explain the presence of sand and derived Tertiary fossils. The Tertiary sands would once have extended far beyond their present limits, extending to the high crests of the Downs. Here they may have undergone extensive modification when they were frozen during glacial episodes of the present Ice Age. Subsequent valley erosion may have left the crestal deposits as isolated relict outliers.

Lower down the slopes are deposits that are described as Brickearth, having once been used for making bricks. Brickearth is massive fine silt. It is believed

to be a wind blown deposit, analogous to the 'loess' silts that extend intermittently along the southern margin of the past ice sheets across Europe and Asia as far as China. It is not generally realized that glacial episodes are times of great aridity because so much water is locked up in the ice sheets. Brickearth has been found both in the Mole Gap and on the banks of its tributaries across the Weald.

Finally the Mole has deposited alluvial sediment as the river meandered to and fro across its flood plain. There is, however, not only alluvium on the present

Building stones of the Mole Valley

Figure 19 a) Bricks and tiles from the Weald Clay

b) Ragstone from the Lower Greensand

c) Carstone from the Lower Greensand

d) Knapped flint from the Chalk

e) Clunch from the Chalk

day flood plain. There are also alluvial terraces above the level of the modern flood plain. These terraces formed when the river was at a higher level. The River Thames has up to 12 terraces, the River Mole merely two. The genesis of river terraces is not well understood, but it is generally accepted that the higher terraces are the oldest, and the lower, that are closest to the modern floodplain, are the youngest. The terrace deposits are generally gravels and, since they contain fossils of woolly mammoth, and other periglacial beasts, it is generally held that they formed during glacial episodes. Dorking Museum has a spectacular collection of bones collected from the terrace gravels of the River Mole. (See Figure 17.)

A peculiar feature of the River Mole is its habit of vanishing through its bed in the Mole Gap. As noted earlier this is not how the River Mole got its name. The Chalk across which the river flows in the Mole Gap is highly permeable due to extensive fractures, enlarged by solution due to acid rain to form swallow holes. (There is nothing new in acid rain. It has always been acidic.) In the Mole Gap there is an abrupt steepening in the gradient of the bed of the river that has formed the locus for fracturing and water loss. The water emerges in springs at Fetcham.

Thus the spectacular scenery of Box Hill and the Mole Valley results from a long and complex history. It is due partly to the differential erosion of alternating hard and soft strata, and partly due to periglacial erosive and depositional processes of the current Ice Age.

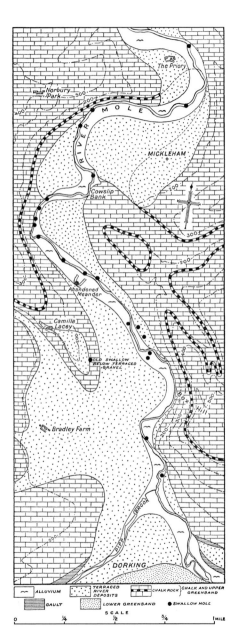

Figure 20 Geological Map of the Mole Gap showing the distribution of swallow holes in and around the river. From Dines & Edmunds 1933. Courtesy of the British Geological Survey

GEOLOGY: KEY TO THE PROSPERITY OF BOX HILL AND THE MOLE VALLEY

The diverse rocks of Box Hill and the Mole Valley have contributed greatly to the prosperity of the area. Beginning a review at the base of the rock sequence, the Weald Clay has provided bricks, as the several brick works south of Dorking testify. Within the Weald Clay, horizons of siderite iron ore (iron carbonate $FeCO_3$) were mined from Roman times onwards, peaking in the 16th and 17th centuries. Thin horizons of Paludina Limestone, cleverly marketed as Purbeck Marble, have been quarried for ornamental building stone.

Above the Weald Clay the Lower Greensand has been important for many reasons. The hard 'ragstone' horizons have been a popular building material. The softer Folkestone sands at the top of the Lower Greensand have been widely used as building sand. In 1931 the *Dorking Advertiser* whimsically reported that the town was 167,900 tons lighter than in 1930; that being the weight of sand removed from the town's quarries in the previous year. The purer sands were also used in glass manufacture. The 'carstone' within the Folkestone sands has been used, occasionally, as a source of iron ore, more widely as a building material, and, when 'galleted' into walls, as an effective witch repellent. The layers of degraded volcanic ash within the Lower Greensand are termed 'fuller's earth'. (Fulling is the process that extracts lanolin from sheep's wool, a necessary precursor to weaving.) But fuller's earth is a particular type of clay that has several other industrial uses. It has been quarried at several places along the Holmesdale to the east of the Mole Valley, notably at Buckland.

Dorking has been a major centre of poultry farming, as testified still by its eponymous five-clawed breed of chicken. Poultry demand well-drained ground, and plenty of grit to aid digestion. The sandy soils of the Surrey Hills provide both. The Lower Greensand in general, and the Folkestone Beds in particular, are a major aquifer, albeit declining at an alarming rate, partly due to climate change, and partly due to excessive abstraction by the inhabitants of Mole Valley. The aquifer of the Lower Greensand is not only very pure, but also produces 'chalybeate' (iron-rich) water. For this reason it has been particularly suited for the cultivation of watercress (*Rorippa nasturtium-aquaticum*, to give it its full and delightful scientific name), believed to be a healthy source of iron. Watercress is not currently grown in the Mole Valley, but the Tillingbourne, as it flows off Leith Hill through Gomshall to join the Wey at Guildford, has hosted watercress beds for hundreds of years. Likewise the greensand waters between Guildford and Alton have also fed watercress beds since time immemorial.

Above the Lower Greensand the soft impermeable Gault clay has provided rich cattle pasture on the floodplains of the Mole and Pipp Brook. Further east along the Holmesdale the Gault Clay has been used for bricks. Its fossils, where concentrated in horizons, have been a source of phosphate fertiliser.

Above the Gault Clay lies the Upper Greensand. It is thin and of little economic importance in the Mole Valley, except in so far as it washes down and lightens the heavy Gault clay. But further east, at Godstone and Reigate, the Upper Greensand has been extensively mined in the past. The well-cemented variety, 'firestone', was used for refractory bricks. The soft variety, 'hearthstone', was used as a domestic abrasive (Sowan, 1975).

Above the thin Upper Greensand is the thick sequence of Chalk of the North Downs through which the Mole has cut its valley on its way to the sea. Chalk is an important source of lime, for building mortar. It is also a fertilizer for the heavy soils of the Gault and London clays and a neutraliser of the acid soil of the Lower Greensand. Thus chalk quarries are a common feature on both the northern and southern limits of the Chalk. They are particularly spectacular along the escarpment of the North Downs on both sides of the Mole Valley. The quarries at Betchworth and Brockham are notable examples, being visible across the Weald for many kilometres. For the most part the Chalk is too soft to serve as a building stone. There are, however, several thin bands of hard well-cemented Chalk that have been quarried for building materials over the years. In the Mole Valley the most important of these is the Chalk Rock at the base of the Upper Chalk. The Chalk Rock was mined for building stone in the Westhumble caves. Galleries were excavated to pursue this stratum deep into the hillside. These caves are now a famously protected bat roost (Greenaway, 2001). Clunch is a term applied to a variety of Chalk used as building stone that is composed of comminuted fragments of

the bivalve *Inoceramus*. Clunch however, has also been applied to a diverse range of soft rubbly rocks used in building. The nodular bands of flint within the Chalk have been of great economic importance, first to provide tools for Stone Age hunters and cave wives, later in flintlock guns, and as a building material. Many buildings in the Mole Valley are built of undressed flint nodules, some of the grandest of flint knapped into cubes. St Martin's Church, Dorking is a fine example, especially when sunlight glances off the fractured flint faces.

Chalk is an important aquifer in the Mole Valley, across the London Basin and indeed across much of southern England. Chalk has a porosity of some 40% and can therefore store large amounts of water. The pores are extremely small, however, and permeability low. (Porosity is a measure of the storage capacity of a rock. Permeability is a measure of the ability of fluid to flow through it.) Chalk is commonly extensively fractured. Fractures impart an extremely high permeability to the Chalk and allow fluid to move in and out of the small pores within the Chalk rock itself. It is for this reason that chalk is such an effective aquifer. It is these same properties that make chalk eminently suitable for viticulture. Vines need a modicum of moisture, but do not like to have their roots waterlogged. Chalk slopes are well drained, due to the permeability imparted by the fractures, but water is stored in the micro-porosity between the fractures. Vine roots may penetrate the fractures and easily access moisture in the water-saturated rock between the fractures. This is why the Champagne region of France is a major centre of viticulture, and why vineyards occur on the Chalk slopes of the Mole Valley at Denbies, which was planted on the recommendation of a notorious local geologist (Selley, 2004).

Figure 21 Fractured chalk from a photograph by the author.

Beyond the Chalk lie the lowlands of the London Clay, the main economic use of which has been for bricks.

To complete this review of the economic importance of the rocks of the Mole Valley it is necessary to describe its subterranean wealth. The earlier account of the uplift and erosion of the Wealden anticline was somewhat simplified. The Wealden basin subsided due to a series of west-east faults in the Earth's crust. The uplift of the Wealden anticline occurred by the reversed movements of these same faults. This inversion formed a series of small anticlines adjacent to the faults. The North Downs is one of these complex faulted alignments, and a series of small oil and gas fields are trapped in anticlines on its southern side. From east to west these include the Palmers Wood oil field at Oxted, the Brockham oil field in the Mole Valley and the Albury gas field further west.

This review shows how the diverse rocks of the Mole Valley have contributed to its past and present prosperity. This prosperity is based not only on the rocks themselves, but also on their contained fluids, their superficial soils, erosion and resultant beautiful scenery.

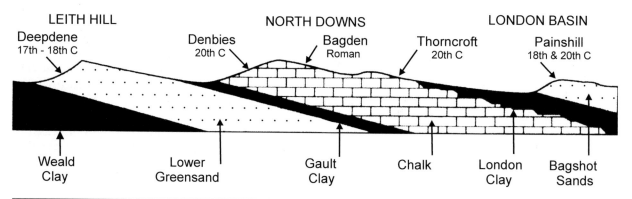

WEALD CLAY	LOWER GREENSAND	GAULT CLAY	UPPER GREENSAND	CHALK	LONDON CLAY
Bricks	Water	Bricks	Firestone	Water	Bricks
Iron	Building Stone	Phosphate	Hearthstone	Flints	
Purbeck marble	Sand		Building stone	Building stone	
	Fuller's earth				
	Glass sand	DEEPER – Oil & Gas in Portland Sand (upper Jurassic)			

ECONOMIC RESOURCES

Figure 22 South to North geological cross-section through the Mole Valley to show the economic resources provided by each rock type. Sites of vineyards that have flourished at various times on sunny south-facing slopes are marked. Thorncroft Manor and part of Denbies vineyards grow on raised Ice Age river gravels of the Mole.

THE FUTURE OF BOX HILL AND THE MOLE VALLEY

Having described the geological processes that have formed Box Hill and the Mole Valley it is appropriate to conclude by considering the future of this beautiful part of Surrey. The immediate future of the area will be controlled by climate change; the more distant future by erosion and earth movements. Studies of rocks from all over the Earth have enabled its history to be reconstructed in great detail for hundreds of millions of years. There is abundant evidence of past climate change, with several major episodes of glaciation. Detailed studies of the younger sediments have shown a gradual cooling of the planet over the last 60 million years, indicating that it entered a new Ice Age some 2 million years ago. Within the present Ice Age there have been many fluctuations of climate during which the British Isles have enjoyed warmer and cooler temperatures than those of today. Geologists used to believe that climatic fluctuations took place gradually over tens of thousands of years. Recent data have revealed, however, that this is false. In fact the alternation from glacial to interglacial episodes happens over tens of years. Data show that the Earth has been warming since the middle of the 19th C. Climate change is largely attributable to cyclic astronomical variations in the Earth's orbit, eccentricity and tilt. Since its establishment by the UN in 1988 the IPCC (Intergovernmental Panel on Climate Change) has published a series of reports on climate change. Research has shown that currently rising temperature cannot be explained by astronomical variables. It does correlate, however, with the rise modelled on the amount of carbon dioxide released into the atmosphere since the start of the Industrial Revolution (Watson, 2001, Houghton,

2004). Scientists have accepted this scenario for a number of years. It has only impacted on the consciousness of politicians and the general public in the last few years, aided by the summers of 2003 and 2006. It is thus possible to speculate on both the immediate and more distant future of Box Hill and the Mole Valley.

The immediate future may be bright. Denbies vineyard was established late in the last century because of the favourable rocks and landscape, and the anticipated beneficial effects of global warming. Soon more vineyards, and even olive groves, may be planted on the sunny south-facing slopes of the Chalk and Lower Greensand, as they were in the past. Gardens will change from traditional English plants to xerophytes more typical of the Mediterranean. Siberia may become the granary of Europe, and Switzerland its rice bowl, with Swiss peasants in coolie hats tending the Alpine rice paddies. The beneficial effects of global warming may only last for a few decades. External environmental pressures beyond the Mole Valley may bring chaos to civilisation across the Earth. Shortages of natural resources will occur as the Earth heats up and deserts expand. Wars will break out as nations fight for food, water, petroleum and other materials. These wars will lead to mass population migration with the concomitant spread of starvation, disease, death and the break down of organised society. A study by the Hadley Centre of The Met Office predicts an average temperature of 46°C in the UK, comparable to the Sahara, by the end of the century. One may fantasize about life in the Mole Valley a hundred years from now:

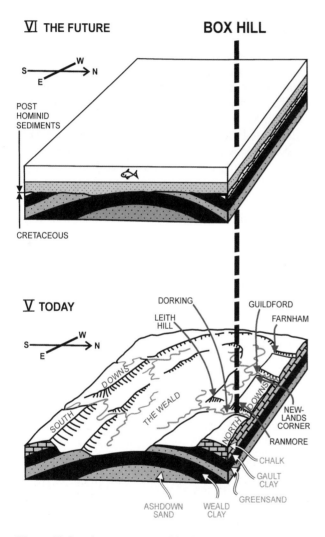

VI THE FUTURE

BOX HILL

W
S — — N
E

POST
HOMINID
SEDIMENTS

CRETACEOUS

V TODAY

DORKING
GUILDFORD
LEITH
HILL
FARNHAM

W
S — — N
E

DOWNS

THE WEALD

SOUTH DOWNS

NORTH DOWNS

NEW-
LANDS
CORNER

RANMORE

CHALK

GAULT
CLAY

GREENSAND

ASHDOWN
SAND

WEALD
CLAY

Figure 23 Geophantasmogram of the future, when Box Hill and the Mole Valley will have been eroded away. The subsidence of the southern North Sea, that has been going on for over 100 million years, aided by global sea level rise, will have caused the flooding of most of England.

August 2106. The sun begins to set over the gleaming white Chalk slopes of the North Downs. Herdsmen gather in the flock of scattered goats that had been grazing all day on such fodder the dying vines, olive and eucalyptus trees can still provide. They hurry. The pack of wild dogs in the Westhumble caves is getter bigger and bolder. Last week they had caught a straggling goat. The herd moves past the oasis at the Meadowbank where onions, aubergines, peppers and tomatoes grow beneath the shade of the date palms. In Dorking High Street people emerge from the cool safety of the cellars and caves that are now their homes, and where too grows Dorking's staple crop of mushrooms. There is a stir and buzz of excitement. A caravan is making its way into the settlement along South Street. This is the first one to cross the Wealden sand sea for several months, the last having been ambushed by bandits from Beare Green. This caravan had detoured westward through the steep-sided wadis that dissect the sandstone jebel of Leith Hill. The camels are hobbled at Pump Corner, now the main rendezvous of the settlement. The caravaneers off load their cargo of salt fish from the coastal ports of Lewes and Billingshurst (the old ports of Newhaven and Chichester were flooded by the rising sea two generations ago). A lively bartering session ensues. Later the caravaneers eat their frugal supper in the White Camel, Dorking's last surviving public house. It is one of the few substantial buildings to have survived the fire that destroyed much of the town in the food riots that followed the famine of 2061. The menu consists of curried goat and Pixham prawns (a local delicacy; actually salt-cured scorpions, a curious five-clawed species peculiar to the area). The old clock over the bar strikes ten. The settlement elders gather beneath a large black glass screen for the daily ritual of 'News at Ten'. Here they exchange the gossip and news of the day. One old man tells that in his grandfather's day faces could be seen on the glass and voices could be heard. No one believes him. There is great excitement because there has been another arrival in the settlement today. A wandering medicine man had led his donkey laden with surgical tools and medicines into the settlement to provide what medical help he can. He has travelled from Goring, established as a small port at the mouth of the Thames after the 'Great Drowning' of 2025 when the Thames Barrier was breached. The medicine man reports that the recent plague epidemic is spent. It was said that there were few survivors left in the West Country, but there is good pasture on the granite uplands of the moors. There was enough grazing not only for goats and camels, but even sheep. The men debate the news. The well at Pump Corner is running dry, and the crops of Meadowbank oasis failing. Should they migrate with their flocks to the West Country for pastures new? The route is dangerous. It lies between the vast sand sea of the New Forest and the barren Chalk downs of Salisbury plain. Few watering holes remain.

Alone in a far corner of the bar Dirty Dick, the old geologist, raises his leather tankard and drains the last of the fermented maize drink that now passes for beer. He wipes the sand and sweat from his beard with his goatskin sun hat and walks out into the High Street. Dirty Dick fans himself with a tattered copy of 'The Box Hill and Mole Valley Book of Geology' while his eyes adjust to the dark. The hobbled camels grunt and burp as they chew their forage. The town watch assembles at Pump Corner for the night patrol, clad in old armour and strange weapons liberated years ago from the antique shops in West Street. Raiders from Reigate might be lurking, waiting to rustle the goats corralled in the old supermarket car park. The feral dog pack howls in the distance. Dirty Dick hobbles off down the High Street to his cave deep beneath the old War Memorial. As he goes he mutters his old refrain through toothless gums: 'We told 'e…we told 'e, you would not listen, and now you are doomed, all doomed d'ye' hear?…'

Moving swiftly on to consider Box Hill and the Mole Valley a few million years from now. Erosion will gradually remove the North Downs and Surrey Hills as the whole of southern England becomes a flat-lying peneplain. The Earth's crust beneath the southern North Sea has been sinking, however, for over a hundred million years, and this subsidence is likely to continue. The sea will continue to flood England's eastern seaboard. The rate of flooding will be enhanced by the global rise of sea levels as the polar ice caps melt and the volume of water in the oceans expands with rising temperature. Above the old easterly tilting land surface of southern England new sediments will be deposited layer-by-layer, just as in the Cretaceous Period, when the history of Box Hill and the Mole Valley began so many millions of years ago.

GEOLOGICAL FAQs

What on Earth is Geology?

Geology is the study of rocks, how they form, the natural resources that they contain, and what they tell us about the past and future history of the Earth. (Geology is not to be confused with archaeology, the study of Pre-historic man.) There are three main classes of rock: igneous, metamorphic and sedimentary. Igneous rocks form from magma originating below the crust of the earth. Magma may erupt at the Earth's surface in volcanoes, giving rise to lavas, or may cool slowly at depth to form coarsely crystalline rock such as granite. Sedimentary rocks include deposits of sand, lime and mud, which on burial become hard strata of sandstone, limestone and shale. Metamorphic rocks are those that have been changed from pre-existing rocks by high temperature, pressure, or both. Sandstone, limestone and shale, for example, metamorphose into quartzite, marble and slate respectively.

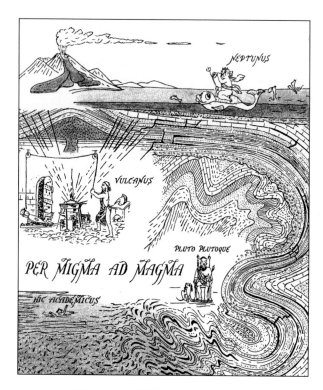

Figure 24 The Rocks Display'd (from Wilson, in Read, 1944), illustrating the formation of igneous, sedimentary and metamorphic rocks on and beneath the crust of the Earth. Courtesy of the Geologists' Association.

Why on Earth study geology?

We inhabit this planet by courtesy of its geology. Geology is essential to understanding the Earth, from tsunamis to town planning. The major problems that face civilization today are future energy supply, climate change, water shortages, coastal erosion, the prediction of tsunamis, super volcano eruptions, and environmental pollution, including the safe disposal of waste, ranging from nuclear to domestic. These problems can only be solved by understanding geology.

What on Earth do geologists do?

Civilisation exists by growing things on the Earth, or extracting minerals and fluids (water and petroleum) from within the Earth. Thus geologists and farmers are the primary wealth creators of society. Geologists find the petroleum that runs your car, the metals of which it is made, the gas that heats your house, and the coal and radioactive minerals that fuel the power stations that provide your electricity. For example, the prosperity of the UK over the past 30 years has been due to the reserves of petroleum found by geologists in the North Sea.

How on Earth do geologists tell the age of rocks?

The relative age of rocks is relatively easy to establish, absolute age is more difficult. In the early 19th C, a surveyor named William Smith was involved in excavating canals and mines all over England, Wales and southern Scotland. Smith discovered that sedimentary strata occur in regular sequences that can be mapped across the countryside, both where they crop out at the surface, and underground from mines and borings. He realised that, except where overturned by folding, the uppermost strata in a sequence of rocks are relatively younger than those that underlie them. He used these data to produce a geological map of much of the UK. (Winchester, 2001) Smith also discovered that fossils occur in a regular sequence within the strata. Even where one type of rock passes laterally into another, limestone into shale for example, the same vertical sequence of fossils is found. Subsequently geologists have discovered that all over the Earth primitive plants, invertebrates, fish, amphibians, reptiles, mammals and hominid fossils are found in progressively superior, and therefore younger, sedimentary strata. On a small scale, animal and plant species evolve and become extinct in a regular sequence that is replicated all over the Earth. These observations are confirmed and refined by geologists on a daily basis. This pattern of the evolution and extinction of fossil species is used to determine the relative ages of rocks. Concomitantly these observations demonstrate that evolution is a fact, not a theory. Charles Darwin's theory of evolution by natural selection is one of several theories advanced to explain the fact of evolution. The belief that the Earth was created in seven days is not consistent with the evidence of fossil evolution, or of plate tectonics, let alone astronomy.

To determine the absolute age of rocks is more complex. Most people accept that the rings seen in the trunk of a tree reflect annual growth, and that ring thickness varies with good and bad seasons. Dendrochronology, as the study of tree rings is termed, has established a sequence of tree rings from living and fossil trees going back over 9,000 years. Annual layers, analogous to tree rings, occur in glacial lake sediments and cores from polar ice caps, continuing a chronology extending back over 400,000 years. (These data present problems for Creation 'Scientists' who believe that the Earth is only some 6,000 years old.) Older absolute dates in deep time going back hundreds of millions of years are calculated from geochemical analyses of rock. These are based on the natural decay of radioactive isotopes to stable isotopes. Decay rates are constant for different mineral systems. Some of the more common methods include carbon-14 analyses, valid back to some 6,000 years. Uranium/thorium/lead and potassium-argon isotopes provide dates going back hundreds of millions of years. The wide range of geochemical techniques enables the validity of the dates they provide to be cross-checked, and their accuracy to be constantly refined.

What on Earth should I do now?

If this book has whetted your appetite to know more about geology, why not join the Mole Valley Geological Society (founded 1975)? Details can be found on **www.dendron.net/mvgs** or contact: Clare Hill, Press & Publicity Officer, The Mole Valley Geological Society, PO Box 425, Dorking, Surrey RH5 4WA. The Mole Valley Geological Society is the local group of the Geologists' Association (details on **www.dendron.net/mvgs**) which was founded in 1858. The GA has a lively group for children called 'Rockwatch' **www.rockwatch.org.uk** The oldest geological society on Earth is The Geological Society of London, founded in 1807. It is mainly for professionals, but its website **www.geolsoc.org.uk** has many useful links.

GEOLOGICAL GLOSSARY

N.B. Many fundamental geological concepts and terms will be found explained in the FAQ section. Here are definitions of some of the geological terms used in this book. *Italicised words are defined elsewhere in the glossary.*

Alluvium, *superficial deposit* laid down by rivers.

Ammonite, an extinct group of marine cephalopods, related to the modern octopus, cuttlefish and squid. Because they evolved rapidly ammonites are important indicators of the relative age of rocks.

Anticline, an upfold of *sedimentary rocks* e.g. the Weald of southeast England.

Boulder Clay, a glacial deposit consisting of clay containing sub-angular stones of many sizes scattered randomly throughout, producing heavy soils throughout East Anglia and parts of the English Midlands.

Carstone, *sandstone* cemented by limonite ($Fe_2O_3.3H_2O$), commonly found in the Folkestone Beds of the *Upper Greensand*, used as a building stone and witch repellent, rarely as an ore.

Chalk, a white friable limestone, highly porous, but of low permeability, unless fractured. Important for viticulture in France and England.

Chalybeate, a type of water rich in iron, and thought to have medicinal properties. The springs of the *Lower Greensand* are commonly chalybeate, due to iron leached out of the glauconite.

Chert, silica (SiO_2) that forms in *sedimentary rocks* after deposition. It occurs replacing fossils and in *nodules* and layers in the *Lower Greensand* and *Chalk* where it is called *Flint*.

Clay, a very fine-grained sediment, generally porous, but impermeable.

Clay-with-flints, a *superficial deposit* of uncertain origin, composed of clay with scattered flints which blankets the top of the *Downs* across much of southern England.

Clunch, a shelly variety of *Chalk*, sometimes termed 'Marlstone', occasionally used as a building stone. The name is also applied to a range of unconsolidated building material of various geological origins.

Concretion, a mineral aggregate that forms within a sediment after deposition. *Flint* concretions are common in *Chalk*.

Coombe Deposits, Coombe Rock, deposits of *Chalk* debris that slid down the *Downs* in periglacial conditions during cold spells of the present Ice Age, termed Coombe Rock when cemented, otherwise friable.

Downs, open rolling countryside with *dry valleys* and scarps composed of Chalk limestone, comparable to the Champagne region of France.

Drift, an obsolete term applied to *superficial deposits* originally thought to be detritus left by the Noarchian flood.

Dry valley, a valley that lacks a river, a characteristic feature of the *Chalk* downlands. Dry valleys formed in periglacial episodes when summer melt water eroded river valleys, being unable to percolate through frozen ground.

Fault, a break in rock with lateral movement.

Flint, a variety of *chert* that forms nodules, often in layers, in the *Chalk*, and in *Clay-with-flints*.

Fossil, literally something that has been dug up. Generally applied to the remains of past animal and plant life, also including tracks, trails and burrows.

Fracture, a break in rock without any lateral movement. Fractures increase the *permeability* of rock.

Geology, Richard, Bishop of Durham in the 14th century divided all knowledge into Geology, the study of Earthly things, as opposed to Theology, the study of Heavenly things.

Glauconite, a green mineral that forms in shallow marine environments. It is glauconite that makes *Greensand* green.

Granite, an igneous rock composed of the minerals quartz, feldspar and mica. It forms from the slow cooling of *magma*.

Greensand, sandstone containing the green mineral *glauconite* that weathers out at the surface to rust (iron oxide).

Hassock, soft strata in the *Lower Greensand*, usually interbedded with *Ragstone*.

Igneous rock, one formed from the cooling of *magma* either cooling slowly underground, giving rise to coarsely crystalline rocks like *granite*, or erupting at the Earth's surface in volcanoes as lava.

Law of superposition, a fundamental principle of geology, that in a sequence of *sedimentary strata* the higher strata are younger than the lower *strata*.

Limestone, a *sedimentary rock* composed of lime (calcium carbonate) of which chalk is a particular variety.

Lithification, the learned term given to describe the process whereby soft sediment is turned into solid rock by temperature and pressure during burial.

Magma, molten material from beneath the earth's surface that cools to form *igneous rocks*.

Marl, a calcareous (lime rich) *clay*.

Metamorphic, a group of rocks formed by high temperature and/or high pressure, from pre-existing rocks, such as *slate*, *schist* and gneiss.

Nodule, a mineral aggregate that forms within a sediment after deposition. *Siderite* nodules are common in the Weald clay.

Permeability, the property of a rock whereby fluid can flow through it. Indicative of interconnected *porosity*.

Porosity, the storage capacity of a rock, generally expressed as a percentage. Pores occur in many ways, some primary, e.g. the spaces between sand grains, others secondary, e.g. *fractures*. At shallow depths pores may be full of air. Below the water table, pores are full of water. Interconnected pores make a rock *permeable*, and allow the flow of water. Pores in very fine sedimentary rocks, such as *clay* and *chalk* may contain water, but be impermeable due to surface tension around the grains. *Fractures*, however, may impart permeability to such rocks.

Quartzite, a metamorphosed *sandstone*, composed almost entirely of the mineral quartz (silica), commonly low in nutrients and highly fractured, and hence permeable.

Rag, or Ragstone, hard well-cemented *sandstone* in the *Lower Greensand* commonly used as a building stone.

River terrace, a flat area on the flank of a river valley above the level of the present flood plain. River terraces are relicts of past flood plains eroded by the river cutting down to its present level. River terraces are composed of admixtures of gravel, sand and clay.

Sand, sediment formed of sand-sized particles, generally of the mineral quartz, silica.

Sandstone, *lithified sand*.

Schist, metamorphosed *clay* transitional between *slate* and gneiss.

Sedimentary rock, rock formed by the *lithifaction of deposits* of grains of *clay, sand* and gravel. Also includes rocks, such as salt, gypsum and dolomite that form by evaporation or replacement of pre-existing sediments.

Series, informal stratigraphic term for a sequence of *sedimentary rocks*, such as the Wealden Series.

Shale, *lithified clay*.

Siderite, the mineral iron carbonate ($FeCO_3$). It occurs as *nodules* in the Weald Clay, and was the ore for the iron industry of the Weald.

Slate, a low-grade metamorphic rock formed when *clay* is subjected to high pressure and temperature, en route from *shale* to *schist*.

Soil, a mixture of organic matter, alive and dead, and weathered rock detritus.

Stratigraphy, the study of sequences of *sedimentary rocks*.

Stratum, single, strata, plural, layer(s) of *sedimentary rock*.

Superficial deposit, shallow sedimentary detritus unrelated to the bedrock that it overlies, includes alluvium, deposited by rivers, and a diverse suite of glacial and periglacial deposits. May be more important to *soil* and viticulture than the bed rock beneath.

Swallow hole, a hole in rock, normally *limestone*, caused by the solution of running water. Swallow holes occur in the River Mole in the Mole Valley.

Syncline, a downfold of *sedimentary rocks*.

Unconformity, a discontinuity between two rock masses due to non-deposition or erosion. The upper is sedimentary, the lower of any origin. Where unconformities separate sedimentary rocks the lower sequence often dips at a steeper angle than the upper strata. An unconformity generally indicates a break in deposition, and hence a gap in time.

Weald, derived from the Old English, meaning 'wild'. There were reports of dragons in the Weald up until the days of Queen Elizabeth I. The Weald gave its name to the Wealden Series. Once a sedimentary basin the Weald is now a large eroded *anticline* that extends across Surrey, Sussex and Kent, and across the channel into France.

REFERENCES

Figure 25 Line drawing by F N Colwell of a flint axe found on Box Hill.

Aubrey, J (1719) *The Natural History and Antiquities of the County of Surrey.*

Brandon, P (2005) *The North Downs.* Phillimore & Co. Chichester. 288pp.

Brayley, E W (1850) *A History of Surrey.* 5 Vols.

Bright, J S (1845). *A History of Dorking.*

Chapman, G M & Young, R H D (1979) *Box Hill.* Serendip Fine Books, Lyme Regis. 165pp.

Denis, J (1855) *A Handbook of Dorking* (2nd Edition). Reprinted by Kohler & Coombes (1974) Dorking. 41pp. ISBN 0 903967 15 4.

Dines, H G & Edmunds, F H (1933) *The Geology of the Country around Aldershot and Guildford* Mem. Geol. Surv. England & Wales. HMSO. 182pp.

Gallois, R W (1965) *British Regional Geology: The Wealden District* HMSO London. 101pp.

Greenaway, F (2001) *The Box Hill Book of Bats* The Friends of Box Hill. Dorking. 42pp.

Houghton, J (2004) *Global Warming. The Complete Briefing* (3rd Edition). Cambridge University Press. Cambridge. 351pp.

Mills, A D (2003) *A Dictionary of English Place-Names* Oxford University Press. Oxford.

Read, H H (1944) *Meditations on Granite* Proc. Geol. Assn. London, Part 2 LV 45-93.

Ruffell, A, Ross, A & Taylor, K (1996) *Early Cretaceous Environments of the Weald* Geologists' Assoc. Guide No. 44. 81pp.

Selley, R C (2004) *The Winelands of Britain.* Petravin Press. Dorking. 109pp. ISBN 0 9547419 0 0.

Selley, R C (2006) *Dorking Caves Guide.* Petravin Press. Dorking. 13pp. ISBN 0 9547419 1 9.

Sowan, P (1975) Firestone and Hearthstone Mines in the Upper Greensand of East Surrey. *Proc. Geol. Ass. London.* V. 86. 571-591.

Sumbler, M G (1996) *British Regional Geology: The Thames Valley.* HMSO London. 173pp.

Timbs, J (1823) *A picturesque promenade round Dorking* 2nd Edition.

Tyson, D E (1979) *A Dorking Childhood – Memories of Old Dorking.* Feldgate, M L (Ed.).

Watson, R T (Ed.) (2001) *Climate Change 2001: Synthesis Report.* Cambridge University Press. Cambridge. 397pp.

Weight, C (1988) *The South Street Caves Dorking.* Dorking & Leith Hill Preservation Society. Dorking. 28pp. ISBN 1 870912 00 4.

White, Rev. G (1789) *The Natural History and Antiquities of Selbourne.* Bickers & Sons. London. 568pp. (And reprinted subsequently by many publishers.)

Winchester, S (2001) *The Map that changed the World* Viking. London. 338pp.

Figure 26 Geological time scale and map of the surface geology of part of the British Isles. Courtesy of the School of Earth Science and Geography, Keele University. The rocks of Box Hill and the Mole Valley were deposited during the Cretaceous Period, the surface distribution of whose rocks are shown in olive green on the accompanying map.